A BIG BOOK, STORIES FROM THE BIBLE

ELAINE M. WARD

Illustrations by Howard Simon

ABINGDON PRESS   New York   Nashville

*To Tommy, Michael, and David
who are different but loved the same*

To Parents and Teachers:

For small children the Bible is just a book. As they hear its stories and learn its message, the Bible will become an important and interesting book. The author hopes this picture book about the Bible will help build toward a later understanding of the Bible as *the* Book.

A BIG BOOK,
STORIES FROM
THE BIBLE

My name is Tommy. People call me "a little boy." They call my brother Bob "a big boy." Mother and Father are big. Grandmother is old.

Each of us is different. Each has a Bible.

Bob's Bible has a red cover. Father carries his Bible in his pocket. Mother keeps hers on a little table beside her bed. Grandmother's Bible is very old.

There are little Bibles and big Bibles. The minister at our church has a big, big Bible.

The Bible at our house is in English. In one place it says, "Love one another." (*John 15:12.*)

Jose's Bible is in Spanish. His Bible says the same thing, "Améis los unos á los otros."

Madelaine's Bible is in French. Her Bible also says, "Aimez-vous les uns les autres."

Gretchen's Bible is in German. Her Bible, too, says, "Liebet euch untereinander."

There are many different Bibles. But each Bible has the same stories.

I like to visit my grandmother. Sometimes we talk about the Bible. One time I asked her, "Where did we get the Bible?"

"Long, long ago," Grandmother said, "people had not learned to read and to write, so they told stories. Many of the stories they told were about God and his plans for the earth and for the people who live here. The stories were remembered carefully and told over and over by many people. A father told them to his sons, and then his sons told the same stories to their sons. When the stories about God were written and put together in a book, it was called a Bible."

"Do you know those stories, Grandmother?" I asked.

"Oh, yes," she answered. "If you will be very still I will tell you one of them, a story about a man named Abraham."

Abraham

Long ago and far away there lived a man named Abraham. He was a shepherd. A shepherd looks after a flock of sheep; he sees that they have plenty of cool water to drink and green grass to eat.

Abraham liked the beautiful land where he lived. He

liked his friends. Abraham loved and trusted God but
other people living near him had not learned to love God.

God told Abraham to take his family and go to another
land. Abraham would have liked to stay where he was,
but he wanted to do whatever God asked him to do. He
loved God.

Abraham and his family left their home. They packed
their clothing and their food on the donkey's backs and

set out for a new land. The women and children rode on
the backs of donkeys. The men walked beside the sheep.
The trip was long.

On and on they traveled. At last Abraham and his family arrived in the new land where they would live.

Abraham wanted to show God that he loved and trusted him. He built an altar. He placed many stones one upon another. There he prayed to God and thanked God for his love.

One day Abraham heard his shepherds fighting with the shepherds of another man named Lot.

"The grass is ours," said Lot's shepherds.

"No, it is our grass," said Abraham's shepherds.

"Stop!" Abraham called to the men. "If you fight the sheep will not be fed. Go back to your sheep, all of you. I will talk with Lot."

Abraham and Lot decided to divide the land.

"You may choose the land you want for your sheep," Abraham said.

Lot chose the best land. But Abraham was not worried. He trusted God. There was grass and water enough for all.

Abraham and his family did not always live in the same place in this new land. Sometimes he would say, "Let us find other grass for our sheep." Again the donkeys would be packed. Abraham and his family would move. But everywhere that Abraham lived he built an altar to show his love for God. (*Genesis 12; 13.*)

"Do you know other stories, Grandmother? What else is in the Bible?"

"The Bible tells us about God," Grandmother answered. "It has stories of people who loved God. The people in the Bible stories were all different but God loved them all. Would you like to hear a story about David?"

"Who was David?" I asked.

"David was a shepherd, too," Grandmother said. "I am going to tell you a story about something that happened when David was just a boy."

David

David was a shepherd boy. As he cared for the sheep, he watched and listened and thought about God's world.

He listened to the soft breeze as it blew the tall grasses where the sheep were eating. It seemed to sing as it blew. David picked up his harp. He sang, "We give thanks to thee, O God; we give thanks."

14

David thanked God for the many good things in his world.

David walked to the brook as the sun became hotter. The water bubbled over the rocks. It seemed to sing as it flowed.

"I give thee thanks, O Lord, with my whole heart," David sang. "I love thee, O Lord, my strength."

David listened to the singing of the birds. They sang as they flew. And David sang as he watched them. He sang, "Make a joyful noise to the Lord, all the lands!"

The birds, the breeze, and the brooks were peaceful.

But it was not always so peaceful for David.

One night as he sat playing soft music on his harp, he heard the rustle of the tall grasses. David looked around quickly. The sheep were sleeping. The wind was still.

Suddenly he heard a loud, angry roar. It was the roar of a mountain lion!

David jumped from the ground. He was a shepherd, and he must protect his sheep. As he felt around on the ground for a big rock, he looked up. He saw the lion ready to leap upon one of the sleeping lambs. David threw the rock with all his strength. The lion roared in pain and ran away into the night.

The little lamb bleated softly as he nestled in David's arms. Again David sang his thanks to God: "I will give thanks to the Lord with my whole heart; I will tell of all thy wonderful deeds." (*Psalms 75:1; 138:1; 18:1; 100:1; 9:1.*)

"That's a good story, Grandmother. Are there more stories about David?"

"Yes, there are others, but we must save those for another time. Your mother wants you to come home now."

"Mother," I called as I ran in the door at my house, "Grandmother has been telling me a story about David and a lion."

"I know," Mother answered. "Grandmother told me on the telephone."

"Do little Bibles have as many stories as big Bibles?" I asked.

"Yes, they can have," Mother said. "The little Bibles have smaller letters, and there are more words on one page. Let me show you." We looked at Bob's little Bible and at Mother's bigger one, but I can't read yet.

"At church we hear stories about Jesus. Are the stories in the Bible?"

"Oh, Tommy!" Mother smiled. "You know there are stories about Jesus in the Bible. Don't you remember the story about the night Jesus was born?"

"Tell it again. Please, Mother!"

The First Christmas

Mary and Joseph were going to Bethlehem. It was a time when many people had to go to the city.

Mary rode on the shaggy, brown donkey. Joseph walked beside them.

Mary sang as she rode,

> O give thanks to the Lord,
>   for he is good;
>   his steadfast love endures for ever!

The trip was long. The sun went down. Soon it would be dark.

Mary was tired. It was time for her baby to be born. The air was cool.

Neither Mary nor Joseph spoke. Then suddenly Joseph cried from the darkness beside Mary, "There is the city!"

Mary could see the lights ahead. Soon there would be a place to rest.

When they came to Bethlehem, they went immediately to an inn. It was the place where travelers stay. But the keeper of the inn said, "We have no room."

"What can we do?" Joseph asked. "My wife is tired. We have been traveling all day."

"There is a stable behind the inn," the innkeeper said. "It is where we keep the animals, but it is clean and warm."

Joseph thanked the man. He helped Mary from the donkey. Inside the stable it was warm and quiet. The little white doves cooed softly. Brown mice scampered about the feet of a gray donkey. An old cow was asleep.

Outside the stable there were many people. Some were buying, and some were selling, and all were hurrying about.

The sky was filled with stars.

Inside the stable it was dark and still.

In the middle of the night the baby was born. Mary wrapped him in soft, warm cloths. She laid him in the manger.

"His name will be Jesus," Mary whispered.

Outside the stable one star shone brighter than all the rest on this first Christmas night.

(Psalms 118:1; Luke 2:4-7.)

That night at the dinner table, I asked my father, "Did you know the Bible has stories about Jesus?"

"I think you are just trying to get me to tell you a story," my father said. "There's the Christmas story—"

"I expect Tommy could tell *you* that one," Mother said. "We talked about it this afternoon."

"But aren't there other stories about Jesus?" I asked.

"Yes, indeed," Father answered. "Let me tell you one about Jesus loving people."

Jesus and the Children

One day Jesus was busy teaching. He said to the people, "God loves you. God cares for the flowers that grow. He cares for the birds that fly. How much more he cares for you."

The people listened to Jesus. They watched the birds flying through the blue skies and forgot their worries. The people smelled the flowers blooming on the hillside and thanked God for his beautiful world.

Jesus loved people. Many came to hear him, mothers, fathers, and children. Jesus told them that God loved them. Jesus wanted the people to love and help one another.

One day Jesus had been teaching since early morning. He heard the children singing. It was good to hear their happy songs. He stopped talking and listened. But now he must go on with his teaching. He heard someone say, "Go away. Jesus has no time for you today."

Jesus turned to see what was the matter. One of his helpers, a disciple, was talking to some mothers, fathers, and their children. The children had stopped skipping and singing.

"Let the children come to me. Do not send them away," Jesus said. "I am never too busy to love little children."

Jesus smiled at the children. He touched them on the head and held them on his lap. The children smiled and were happy again as Jesus told the people, "And God loves you." (*Matthew 19:14-15.*)

"Were there many, many children with Jesus that day?" I asked my father. "Little ones and bigger ones?"

"Yes," he answered. "Little ones and bigger ones. Children with blue eyes, children with dark eyes, fair skin, and dark skin. Many children."

"Tell me another story about Jesus!"

"Tommy, Tommy!" My father laughed. "Do you want to hear all the stories in one night?"

"Could I? All the stories in one night?"

"No, there are far too many. But I'll tell you one more tonight. One about Jesus helping people."

The Five Friends

One day Jesus was in a home preaching. Many people were in the house with him. There were so many people no one else could come in. There was no room for anyone else even around the door.

Five men came toward the house. They had heard that Jesus was there. But only four men were walking. One man could not walk. His friends were carrying him on a mat. They were coming to ask Jesus to help their friend who could not walk. When they reached the house where Jesus was, the men could not get near Jesus because of the crowd.

"What shall we do?" the four men asked each other. "We must see Jesus."

"We can wait until the crowd goes homes," said one.

"We can go home and come another day," said the second friend.

"No, we must find a way to see Jesus today," said the third friend.

"There is a way," said the fourth friend, pointing to the stairs outside the house.

The four men climbed the stairs to the roof. Together they carried their friend. Then together they made an opening in the roof. They lowered their friend on his mat through the opening.

Jesus looked up when he heard the noise. He was surprised when he saw a man coming down through the roof. He was pleased when he saw that the four men wanted to help their sick friend. The good friends were sure that Jesus could help them.

Jesus took the sick man's hand. He helped him rise from his mat.

"I say to you, stand up," Jesus said. "Take your mat and go home. You are well."

The five men thanked Jesus. Now five men walked out of the house and down the street.

One, two, three, four men were happy as they returned home. But the fifth man, with his mat under his arm, was the happiest of them all.

(Mark 2:11-12.)

28

My brother Bob is a big boy. I think he is ten years old. And he can read. He told me a story about Jesus forgiving people. It is the story about Zacchaeus.

Zacchaeus

Zacchaeus was a rich man. He had a big house and fine clothes and much money. But he was not happy. He was lonely. He had no friends.

Some people visited Zacchaeus but they were not his friends. They liked him only because he was rich.

The people did not like Zacchaeus because they were afraid of him. He was not honest. He cheated people. He kept money that did not belong to him. Zacchaeus liked money more than he liked people, but he was lonely and unhappy.

One day Zacchaeus heard that a man named Jesus was coming through his town.

"Jesus is a kind man," said the people. "Jesus loves everyone, even those who do wrong."

Zacchaeus listened to the people talk. He wanted to see this man called Jesus.

"Jesus is coming!" the people cried. "Jesus is coming!" the children shouted.

Zacchaeus looked around. He was a short man and even on his tiptoes he could not see over the heads of the people near the road.

Zacchaeus saw a tree. He ran to it. He climbed into the highest branch. Zacchaeus wanted to see Jesus.

Jesus wanted to see Zacchaeus, too. When he reached the tree in which Zacchaeus sat, Jesus said, "Come down from the tree, Zacchaeus. I am going to your house today."

Zacchaeus climbed down and led Jesus to his home.

"Why would Jesus want to go to Zacchaeus' house?" some of the people asked.

"Doesn't Jesus know that Zacchaeus has not been honest?" asked others. "Should we tell Jesus that he has done wrong?"

Jesus knew that Zacchaeus had done wrong. He knew

also that he was sorry. Jesus knew that Zacchaeus needed his help, and Jesus wanted to be his friend.

When Jesus left Zacchaeus' home, Zacchaeus had a friend. Jesus loved him as if he had done no wrong. Jesus forgot the bad things he had done and forgave him.

To show that he was sorry, Zacchaeus returned the money he had taken from others. He gave them back even more than he had taken. He wanted to show that he loved God too. For now people and friends were more important to Zacchaeus than money.

(Luke 19:1-10.)

"Does God forgive people too?" I asked when Bob had finished with the story about Zacchaeus.

"Yes," Bob said. "Because God loves us, he forgives us. Jesus told a story that shows how God is like a loving father."

The Father

A father had two sons whom he loved very much. The younger son decided he wanted to go away from home. His father gave him money, but he was sorry to see his son leave. The man loved his son very much.

The son went away. Before many weeks had passed he had spent all the money his father had given him. He was lonely and afraid. He wanted to return home but was afraid to go because he had done wrong.

At last he said, "I will go home and tell my father I am sorry. I will ask him to forgive me. I cannot be his son again but perhaps he will let me be a servant in his house."

The father saw his son coming down the road a long way off. He ran to him, glad that he had returned, for he loved his son. He asked him to be his son again and to stay with him always.   (*Luke 15:11-24.*)

There are many Bibles. Little ones, big ones—the biggest I ever saw is the one our minister uses at church. Once when my class visited the sanctuary in church, the minister told us a story from the Bible.

The First Easter

Jesus loved and helped people. But there were some who did not like what Jesus said.

"You do not love God," Jesus told them. "You love yourselves instead of God. You rob the poor to build a beautiful temple not for God but for yourselves."

The people were very angry. How could they stop this man Jesus from talking this way? They must stop him!

But Jesus was speaking the truth. He wanted these men

to change. He wanted them to be sorry. He wanted them to love God. Jesus would not stop talking to them.

"Please, Jesus, stop saying these things that make the people angry," his friends begged.

"I am not afraid. God is with me," Jesus replied. "I have been sent from God."

When the angry men heard Jesus say that he was from God, they did not believe him. They decided that Jesus must be killed.

So Jesus was put to death on a cross. And when he was dead, his friends placed him in a tomb. Sadly they placed a rock before the tomb. Now they were alone. They felt that without Jesus they could not teach about God.

Three days later, on a Sunday, two of Jesus' friends went to the place where they had put his body. But the body was not there. Jesus was not in the tomb!

With great joy the women ran to tell the other friends of Jesus. Soon all the friends of Jesus had heard the good news.

"Jesus lives! Jesus lives today! Jesus will live forever!"

They told the good news to everyone. "Jesus lives today!" they said. "Jesus will live forever." (*Luke 24.*)

Another time the minister told us a story about Timothy. "Many different people in the Bible told about God and his love," said the minister. "One of those people was Timothy. This is a story of Timothy as a boy."

Timothy's Birthday

One. Two. Three. Four. Five. Six! Timothy had a birthday. Today Timothy was six years old.

"You are growing up, Timothy," his grandmother, Lois, said.

"Soon you will go to school," said his mother, Eunice.

"Then I can read from the scroll," Timothy said.

Timothy's grandmother often read to him from the scroll that was their Bible. Timothy knew most of the stories by heart. Yet he was glad he soon would learn how to read. He would be able to read the stories to others. He would read them the stories about things God had done.

Now that he was a year older there were more things Timothy would be able to do.

"Timothy," called Mother Eunice. Timothy forgot his birthday for a moment. He ran to his mother.

"Timothy," she said, "your grandmother does not feel well today. This is the day she reads from the scroll to Rachel who cannot see. Would you read to Rachel?"

Timothy looked at his mother. "I cannot read," he said, "but I remember the stories. I will go."

"Thank you, Timothy," said his mother.

As he went out the door, Grandmother Lois called. "Here," she said, "take my scroll. Thank you, Timothy."

Timothy could not read, but he felt very big carrying the scroll. He would tell Rachel all the stories about God that he could remember.

Timothy was very happy as he walked along. He was getting to be a big boy. And someday he would tell the stories of God's love to many people.

"The Bible tells us many things, doesn't it?" I said to my mother.

"Yes," she said, "the Bible tells us how God wants us to live."

"Sometimes we don't like to share," said my brother Bob, "but Jesus said, 'Love one another.' " (*John 15:12.*)

"Sometimes we forget, or we hurry too much," said Grandmother, "but the Bible says, 'Stand still, think of the wonders of God.' "   (*Job 37:14.*)

"Sometimes we worry," said Mother, "but Jesus says in the Bible, 'God cares about you.' "   (*I Peter 5:7.*)

"The Bible is an important book," said my father. "It is different from other books, but it is for everyone."

"Even me?" I asked.

"Even you," said my father. "And here is a Bible that you may have when you learn to read."